Michał Rusinek
Little Chopin

Translation by Antonia Lloyd-Jones
Illustrated by Joanna Rusinek

znak

THE
FRYDERYK
CHOPIN
INSTITUTE

Dearest little Boys and Girls,

you know that it wouldn't strain us
to look round and find a statue
representing someone famous.

Here's a fellow up on horseback –
he's got wings that look like sails.
There's a lady with a shield,
and a mermaid's scaly tail.

Over there beneath that tree trunk,
by the pond that looks quite inky,
sits a chap with head turned sideways,
as if smelling
something stinky.

Have you ever stopped to wonder
who these famous folk might be?
Or what they did when they lived here,
when they weren't just sitting tightly?

I will tell you a big secret –
quiet now, but the people who are
represented in the statues
once were children,

just like you are.

For example Frédéric Chopin
– we've met him by the pond already –
used to be young Master Fred, or
even smaller little Freddy.

As a child, just like his statue
he would pull an ugly face
when for dinner every Tuesday
spinach – yuk – made him grimace.

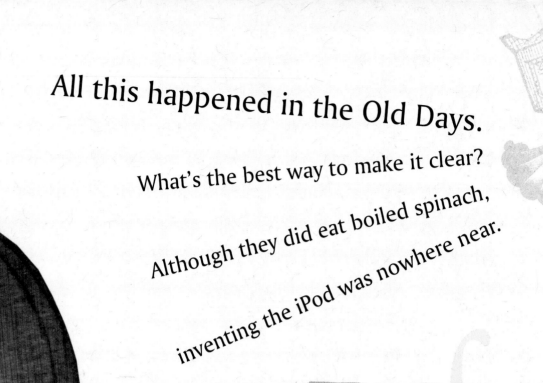

All this happened in the Old Days.

What's the best way to make it clear?

Although they did eat boiled spinach,

inventing the iPod was nowhere near.

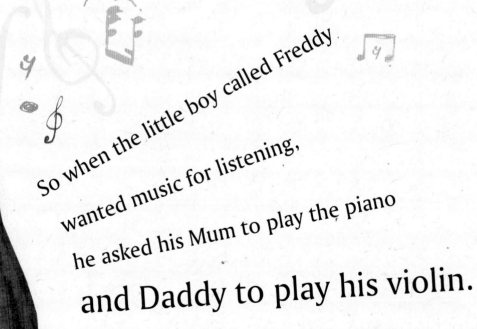

So when the little boy called Freddy

wanted music for listening,

he asked his Mum to play the piano

and Daddy to play his violin.

Freddy's Dad was born in France, where
words are said in a funny way,
not at all how they are written,

but to the French

they sound
OK.

When a person is called "Chopin",
even though it starts with a "ch",
it's pronounced "Sho-pan" or "Sho-pa"…
It's a Frenchman's national feature.

Freddy and his three young sisters,
Mister Chopin and his spouse,
lived in Poland by a river,
in a great big country house.

Freddy used to like the same games
all you children love to play.
He made tiny boats from tree bark,

then

he watched them

float away.

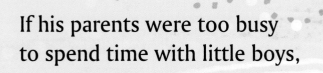

If his parents were too busy
to spend time with little boys,

he would walk in woods and meadows,
listening to nature's noise.

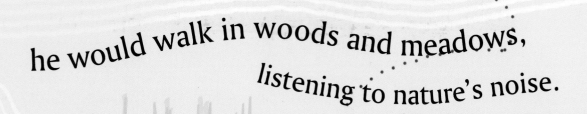

One day Fred was fully focused
on nature's sounds, when suddenly –
hundreds of savage ants were on him,
the kind that eat children for their tea.

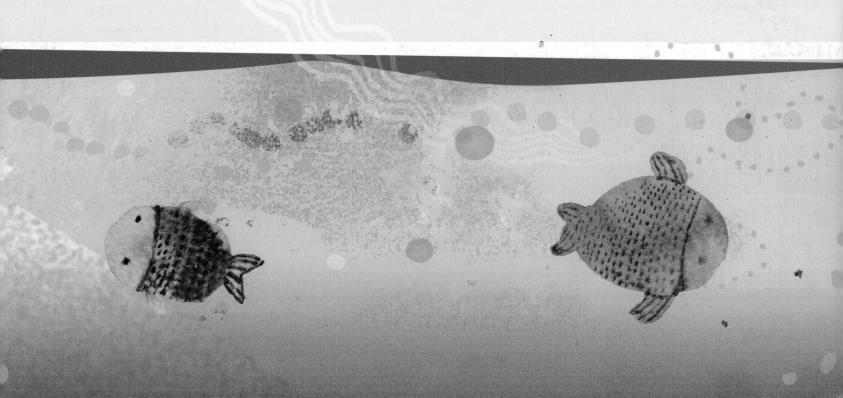

Do you think that he was frightened?
Never – the Chopins are famously brave.

He shook and he shook till the ants fell off
onto a page with a musical stave.

Then he slammed his

notebook shut

and ran home quick. That afternoon
he showed his folks the squashed ants' page,
and they began to hum a tune.

And when they said congratulations
for writing his first ever MARCH
the ants woke up, and in a neat line
they marched off
across the porch

And so Fred's
first composition
vanished from the page forever.
But those ants in his pants marching –
could young Fred forget them?
Never!

But he didn't need more help from
creepy bugs that make you ill,
though he got the birds to aid him –
writing notes with
a feather quill.

One early morning Fred got up
when it was still dark in the manor.
Rubbing his eyes on his way to the loo

he bumped into

the grand piano.

For grand pianos like to prowl
about the house while people snore
(all day they stand and keep quite still
to let you play – that's what they're for).

They have three legs,
a great long body,
and huge wide jaws like a crocodile.
Eighty-eight teeth grin out at you—
and sometimes they ring instead of smile.

When this monster whacked our Freddy,
it gave out a mournful groan.
Fred was worried for the creature—
"Maybe the toothache is making
it moan?"

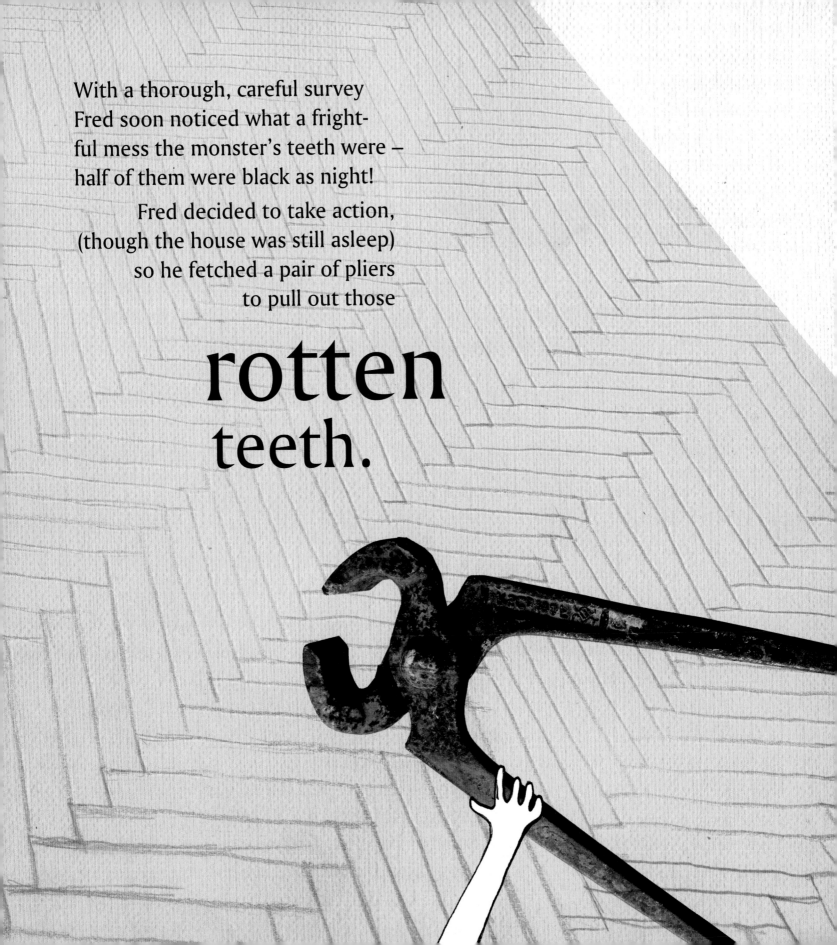

With a thorough, careful survey
Fred soon noticed what a fright-
ful mess the monster's teeth were –
half of them were black as night!
Fred decided to take action,
(though the house was still asleep)
so he fetched a pair of pliers
to pull out those

rotten
teeth.

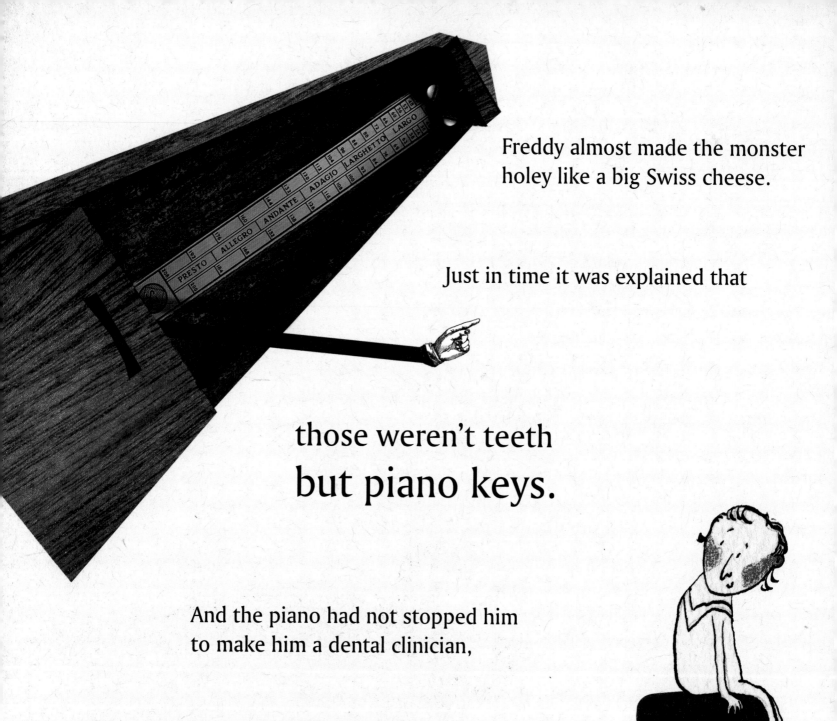

Freddy almost made the monster
holey like a big Swiss cheese.

Just in time it was explained that

those weren't teeth
but piano keys.

And the piano had not stopped him
to make him a dental clinician,

but wanted, as young Freddy's friend,
to teach him to be a top musician.

This three-legged teacher quickly taught him
all the skills that it possessed,
all about rhythm,
scales
and tempos,
octaves,
fifths,
and flats,
and rests.

It taught him how to play upon it
music by other composers too,
as well as to write his very own pieces
on a stave all blank and new.

After such a course young Freddy
was rightly called a prodigy,
and if it had yet been invented,
he'd have been on the TV.

In those days there were no reporters
to put him in the public glare,
so he could play in peace and quiet,
with his toys or his musical flair.

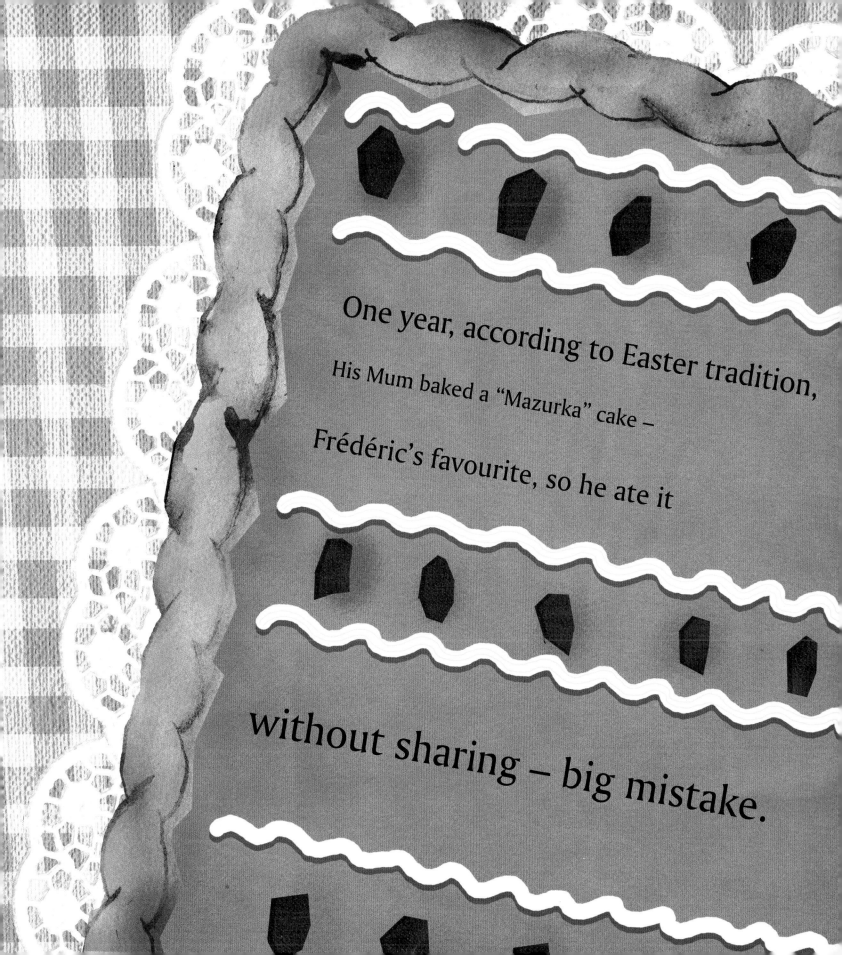

One year, according to Easter tradition,
His Mum baked a "Mazurka" cake –

Frédéric's favourite, so he ate it

without sharing – big mistake.

He got into trouble, and found out
stomach-cake just isn't yummy –
all night he felt like costumed couples
were dancing about

in his tummy.

He listened to his tummy's rhythms –
those were the dances we call "folk"!
He heard the Mazur, the Oberek,
then the Kouyaviak – and awoke.

At once he made up two MAZURKAS
– but not the kind for gobbling;
when these are played on a piano,
they sound like Fred's tummy wobbling.

Dances?
For boys?
You must be joking!

But children, you must not forget
that in the days when Frédéric lived
the engine wasn't invented yet.

And so there weren't yet any cars –
neither parked nor revving their motors,
no Polonez-es – a Polish make –
no imported Jeeps and no Toyotas.

In other words, if our friend Freddy
had wanted to take his driving test,
he'd have to wait a hundred years
for cars to be made – that long at least.

But he wasn't quite so patient,

so – crunching on meringue aux fraises –

he worked hard, and in a fortnight

he composed two POLONAISES.

The Polonaise is a folk dance tune
– Polish, as you won't be slow to
guess – that copies the pace of walking,
not the rhythm of a motor.

Motors are motors and cars are cars,
but don't you children always holler:
"Wow! Amazing! That is awesome!"
when you see a big steam-roller?

But nothing rolled in Chopin's lifetime

quite like the Waltz – you know it for sure –

yes, it's a tune that couples dance to

on a parquet ballroom floor.

Waltz time is not like the beat of this poem –
on it rolls, on it rolls, on it rolls fast –
just like a train when it's racing to get there
(though there were none of those then in the past).

So Fred didn't sit there staring

at all kinds of new machine,

but he made up lots of WALTZES,

sounding lovely and serene.

Once he wrote a graceful RONDO —

that means round, just like a ring —

though a Rondo's not for wearing

but, like all tunes, for listening.

The Rondo is quite like a song
(it has no words – no need for learning)
because it has a fixed refrain
that's like **a boomerang** returning.

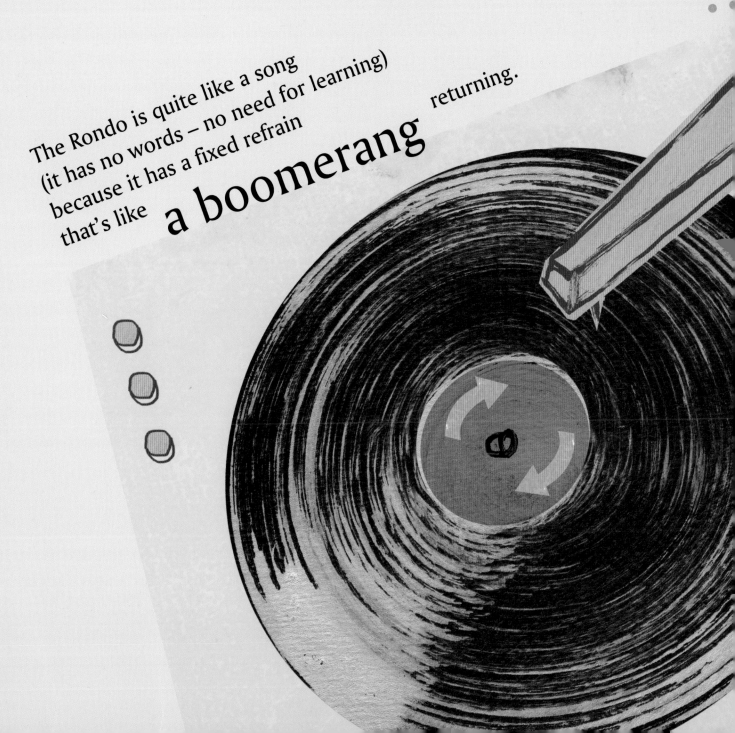

So let's get back to Frédéric,
who always was a mucky pup.
His hands were inky from composing,

but one fine day – he was

grown

up!!

That gorgeous child was gone forever,
but what happened? Quite a rare thing –
Fred was gorgeous as a grown-up,
everybody's favourite darling.

He toured the world, performing concerts
and composing lovely tunes or
teaching others how to play them,
as had done his three-legged tutor.

If he was homesick he wrote letters
(never texts – he had no phone).
Until he came back home forever,
as a statue made of stone.

So he sits quietly by the duck pond –
there in comfort, turning his head, he
remembers life as Master Fred,

or even smaller little
Freddy.

Original title: *Mały Chopin*

Cover and graphic design: Joanna Rusinek

Copyright © by Michał Rusinek
Copyright © for the English translation by Antonia Lloyd-Jones

paperback:
 ISBN 978-83-61142-07-2
 ISBN 978-83-240-1085-1
hardcover:
 ISBN 978-83-240-1108-7

www.znak.com.pl
www.chopin.nifc.pl
www.michalrusinek.pl

Printed in Poland by Colonel, Cracow